GW00659441

recorder ②

for descant recorder and piano

für Sopranblockflöte und Klavier

brian bonsor

www.universaledition.com

vienna · london · new york

UE 19 364

ISMN M-008-03898-3
UPC 8-03452-02205-3
ISBN 978-3-7024-2661-3

JAZZY SERIES

Young players of today are exposed to a variety of contemporary styles and this new series of jazzy and relaxing pieces for PIANO, FLUTE, CLARINET, SAXOPHONE, RECORDER and VIOLIN, attempts to provide players with experience of the syncopated patterns of Jazz, Rock and Pop music, whilst keeping within technical bounds which will have been achieved at various grades. Where appropriate, accompaniments have been kept deliberately simple to encourage other young players to act in this capacity.

Heutige junge Musiker sind einer Vielfalt zeitgenössischer Stile ausgesetzt. Diese neue Serie von jazzigen und entspannenden Stücken für KLAVIER, FLÖTE, KLARINETTE, SAXOPHON, BLOCKFLÖTE und VIOLINE will versuchen, die Spieler mit der Praxis der synkopierten Muster in Jazz, Rock- und Popmusik vertraut zu machen, innerhalb der technischen Möglichkeiten, die schrittweise erreicht werden sollen.
Wo es zweckmäßig schien, wurden die Begleitstimmen absichtlich einfach gesetzt, um dadurch andere junge Musiker zum Mitspielen anzuregen.

A further five pieces in various jazz/swing styles, only slightly more demanding, technically, than those in Book 1, and forming a useful set of studies in different tonguings, ranging from the rhythmic, almost percussive tonguing needed for No. 1 to the warm, flowing legato appropriate to No. 4.

Note-values should not always be interpreted too literally – it is virtually impossible to write down jazzy music as it should be played – but that should not be taken as an invitation to stray too far from the printed text, or to alter the melodies. Played with the correct sense of style, these pieces will provide effective, enjoyable and 'different' concert/festival material for intermediate players.

Grade: 4 – 5

Fünf neue Stücke in verschiedenen Jazz- und Swingstilen, die technisch nur etwas anspruchsvoller sind als jene in Band 1. Sie stellen wertvolle Studien zu verschiedenen Zungentechniken dar, angefangen von der rhythmischen, fast schlagenden Technik, die für Nr. 1 erforderlich ist, bis hin zum warmen, fließenden Legato, das man für Nr. 4 braucht.

Die Notenwerte sollten nicht allzu wörtlich genommen werden. Es ist praktisch unmöglich, Jazzmusik genau so zu notieren, wie sie ausgeführt werden soll. Das eben Gesagte sollte jedoch nicht als Einladung aufgefasst werden, zu weit vom gedruckten Text abzuweichen oder gar die Melodien zu ändern. Mit dem richtigen Stilgefühl ausgeführt, stellen diese Stücke wirkungsvolles, originelles Material für Konzerte dar, an dem jeder Spieler mit mittleren technischen Fertigkeiten viel Spaß haben wird.

Schwierigkeitsgrad: 3 (Skala 1 – 5)

CONTENTS

To my friend Paul Clark in admiration

JaZZy ReCoRdER 2

①

GET UP AND GO!

BRIAN BONSOR

Universal Edition UE 19364

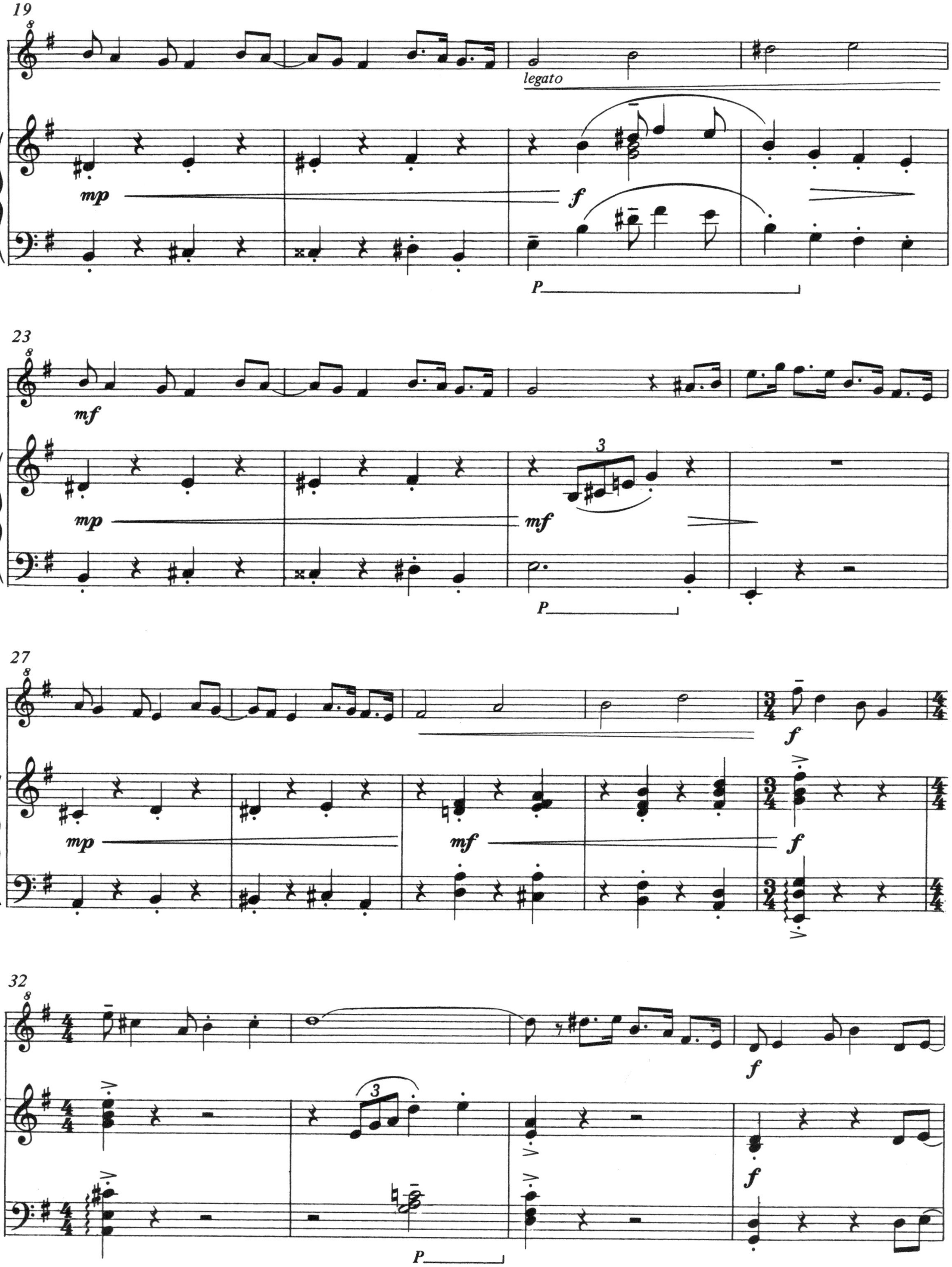
19
legato
23
27
32

4

(2)

NICE 'N' EASY

With an easy swing (♩ = c. 108)

BRIAN BONSOR

★ Third note on the beat,
here and elsewhere.

(con Ped.)

③
SERENATA

Tempo di Beguine (♩ = c. 132)

BRIAN BONSOR

12

REVERIE

Tempo rubato e molto flessibile (♩ = c. 84)

BRIAN BONSOR

★ See page 4

16

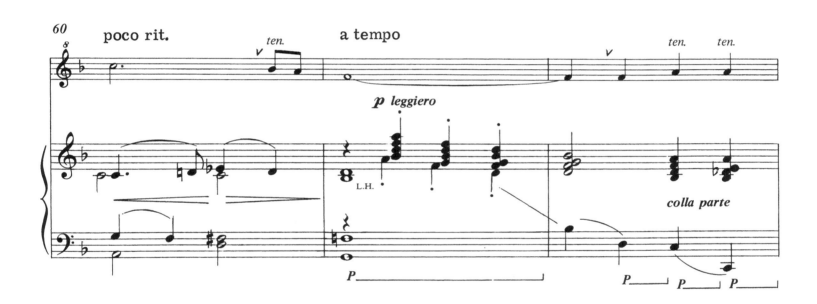

WALTZ FOR MO

BRIAN BONSOR